The Queen's New Crown

Written by Lisa Thompson

Pictures by Andy and Inga Hamilton

The Queen's old crown was broken. She needed a new one.

The King asked the people to make the Queen a new crown.

2

The people who lived by the sea talked to the pearl divers.

The pearl divers found the best pearls in the sea.

The Queen tried on the round crown with lots of white pearls.

"No, no, no," said the Prince. "It is too round and too white."

6

The people who lived on the mountain talked to the gem miners.

The gem miners dug the best gems out of the mountain.

9

The Queen tried on the square crown with lots of gems.

"No, no, no," said the Princess. "Square is the wrong shape for a crown."

11

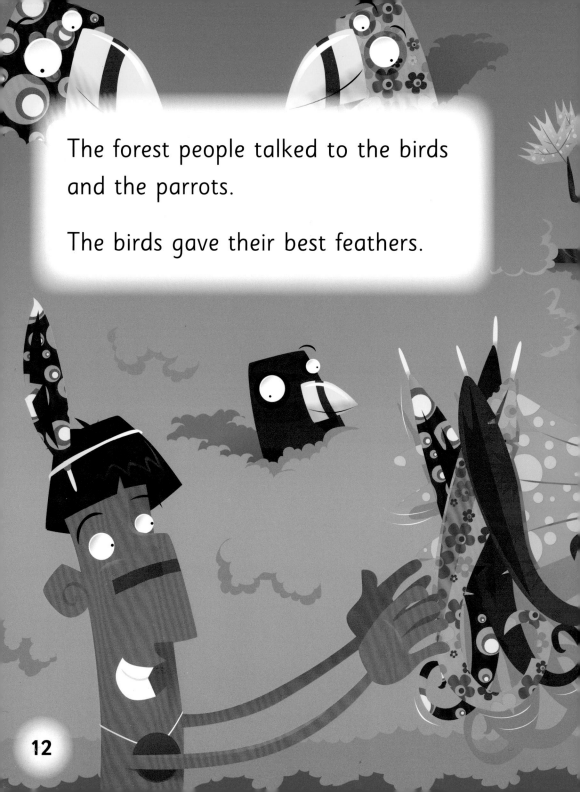

The forest people talked to the birds and the parrots.

The birds gave their best feathers.

The Queen tried on the very tall crown made of feathers.

"No, no, no," said the King. "That crown is much too tall."

The people who lived on the plains talked to the gold miners.

The gold miners found the very best gold in the streams.

The Queen tried on the small crown made of gold.

"No, no, no," said the King.
"That crown is too small and too gold."

18

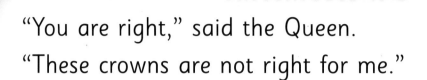

"You are right," said the Queen. "These crowns are not right for me."

A young knight arrived. He handed the Queen a box. "Your Majesty, I have travelled all over the kingdom for your new crown."

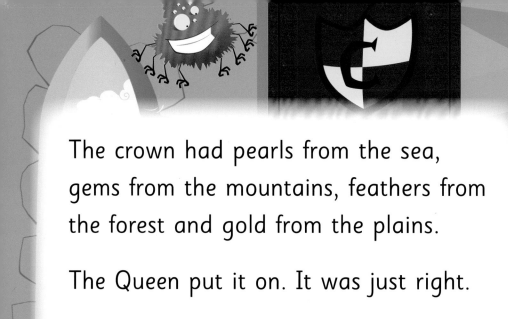

The crown had pearls from the sea, gems from the mountains, feathers from the forest and gold from the plains.

The Queen put it on. It was just right.

"This is a crown from all over the kingdom," said the Queen.